BIBLEFORCE®

JESUS LIVES!

THE STORY OF SALVATION

The Birth of Christ

Matthew 2; Luke 1-2

MARY LIVED IN A TOWN CALLED NAZARETH. SHE WAS ENGAGED TO A CARPENTER NAMED JOSEPH. ONE DAY, AN ANGEL APPEARED BEFORE HER AND TOLD HER THAT GOD HAD CHOSEN HER FOR A SPECIAL HONOR. "YOU WILL GIVE BIRTH TO A SON," HE SAID, "AND YOU ARE TO CALL HIM JESUS. HE WILL BE GOD'S OWN SON AND HIS KINGDOM WILL NEVER END!" IT HAPPENED AS THE ANGEL HAD SAID.

AROUND THIS TIME, THE EMPEROR OF ROME ORDERED A CENSUS OF ALL HIS PEOPLE. JOSEPH AND MARY HAD TO TRAVEL TO BETHLEHEM, THE HOME OF JOSEPH'S ANCESTORS. THE JOURNEY WAS LONG, AND WHEN THEY ARRIVED IT WAS SO BUSY THAT THE ONLY PLACE THEY COULD FIND TO STAY WAS A STABLE. THERE MARY'S BABY WAS BORN.

THAT SAME NIGHT, SHEPHERDS IN THE NEARBY HILLS WERE VISITED BY AN ANGEL WHO TOLD THEM OF THE NEWBORN SAVIOR. THEY HURRIED DOWN TO BETHLEHEM, AND THERE THEY FOUND THE BABY LYING IN A MANGER. THEY WERE FILLED WITH JOY!

IN A DISTANT LAND, SOME WISE MEN WHO HAD BEEN STUDYING THE SKIES, FOLLOWED ONE SPECIAL STAR ALL THE WAY TO JUDEA. IT WAS A SIGN THAT A GREAT KING HAD BEEN BORN. IN JERUSALEM THEY ASKED KING HEROD WHERE THEY COULD FIND THE BABY WHO WOULD BECOME KING OF THE JEWS. HEROD'S ADVISORS TOLD HIM OF A PROPHECY THAT THE NEW KING WOULD BE BORN IN BETHLEHEM, SO THE KING SENT THE WISE MEN THERE, SAYING, "ONCE YOU HAVE FOUND HIM, TELL ME WHERE HE IS, SO I CAN VISIT HIM TOO!" BUT HEROD REALLY WANTED TO MAKE SURE THE BABY DIDN'T BECOME KING.

THE WISE MEN FOLLOWED THE STAR TO BETHLEHEM. THEY KNELT BEFORE JESUS AND PRESENTED HIM WITH GIFTS. THEN THEY RETURNED STRAIGHT HOME—FOR GOD HAD WARNED THEM IN A DREAM NOT TO TELL HEROD WHERE THE BABY WAS.

WHEN THE WISE MEN DIDN'T RETURN, HEROD GAVE AN ORDER THAT ALL BOYS UNDER THE AGE OF TWO IN BETHLEHEM SHOULD BE KILLED—FOR HE WAS DETERMINED THERE SHOULD BE NO OTHER KING! BUT AN ANGEL WARNED JOSEPH IN A DREAM, AND HE AND MARY FLED WITH BABY JESUS TO EGYPT. WHEN HEROD DIED, THEY RETURNED HOME TO NAZARETH. AS THE YEARS PASSED, JESUS GREW AND WAS FILLED WITH GRACE AND WISDOM.

WHY? WHY WOULD JESUS DO IT? WHY WOULD THE SON OF GOD LEAVE THE WONDERS AND GLORIES AND PERFECTION OF HEAVEN TO COME TO EARTH? HE IS THE KING OF ALL KINGS, AND YET HE WAS BORN A HELPLESS BABY IN A COMMON STABLE.

WHY? HE DID IT FOR YOU.

GOD'S LOVE FOR YOU IS SO IMMENSE, SO HUGE AND ENDLESS THAT HE SENT HIS OWN SON TO SHOW YOU THE WAY—THE WAY TO LIVE, THE WAY TO LOVE, AND THE WAY TO HEAVEN. THAT'S WHY JESUS CAME.

The Baptism, the Temptation and the Calling of the Disciples

Matthew 3–4, 10

JESUS' COUSIN JOHN HAD BEEN PREACHING IN THE WILDERNESS. MANY TRULY REPENTED, AND JOHN BAPTIZED THEM IN THE RIVER JORDAN, AS A SIGN THAT THEIR SINS HAD BEEN WASHED AWAY, AND THAT THEY COULD START AFRESH.

JESUS CAME TO BE BAPTIZED. JOHN WAS SHOCKED. "YOU SHOULDN'T BE ASKING ME TO BAPTIZE YOU!" HE EXCLAIMED. "I SHOULD BE ASKING YOU TO BAPTIZE ME!"

BUT JESUS INSISTED. WHEN JESUS CAME UP FROM THE WATER, THE HEAVENS OPENED AND THE SPIRIT OF GOD DESCENDED ON HIM LIKE A DOVE. AND A VOICE FROM HEAVEN SAID, "THIS IS MY SON, WHOM I LOVE; WITH HIM I AM WELL PLEASED."

AFTER THIS JESUS SPENT FORTY DAYS AND NIGHTS IN THE DESERT AS A TEST. HE ATE NOTHING. THE DEVIL CAME TO HIM AND TRIED TO TEMPT HIM. HE ASKED JESUS WHY HE DIDN'T TURN THE STONES TO BREAD IF HE WAS THE SON OF GOD, OR SHOW HIS POWER IN OTHER WAYS TOO. AT LAST SATAN OFFERED HIM ALL THE KINGDOMS OF THE WORLD, IF JESUS WOULD SIMPLY BOW DOWN AND WORSHIP HIM.

BUT JESUS CALMLY TOLD HIM TO GO AWAY. "AWAY FROM ME!" HE SAID. "FOR IT IS WRITTEN, 'WORSHIP THE LORD YOUR GOD, AND SERVE HIM ALONE.'"

WHEN THE DEVIL REALIZED THAT HE COULD NOT TEMPT JESUS HE LEFT, AND GOD SENT HIS ANGELS TO HELP JESUS TO RECOVER.

JESUS RETURNED TO GALILEE AND BEGAN TO PREACH. HE GATHERED AROUND HIM A FEW MEN WHO BECAME HIS VERY SPECIAL FRIENDS AND COMPANIONS. THEY WERE KNOWN AS HIS DISCIPLES. THEY LEFT THEIR FAMILIES AND HOMES AND JOBS TO TRAVEL WITH JESUS. SOME OF THE DISCIPLES WERE FISHERMEN, SUCH AS SIMON (ALSO CALLED PETER), HIS BROTHER ANDREW, AND THEIR FRIENDS JAMES AND JOHN. JESUS TOLD THEM TO LEAVE THEIR NETS AND INSTEAD BECOME FISHERS OF MEN! AND THEY DID.

ALTOGETHER THERE WERE A DOZEN SPECIAL DISCIPLES WHO FOLLOWED JESUS AND LEARNED FROM HIM. SOMETIMES JESUS SENT THEM OUT TO HEAL AND PREACH THROUGHOUT THE REGION.

JESUS WAS NOT ONLY GOD, HE WAS ALSO A MAN. AS A MAN, HE WAS TEMPTED BY THE DEVIL IN EVERY WAY THAT YOU ARE—BY HUNGER, BY POWER, BY WEALTH, AND EVEN BY THE DESIRE TO PROVE WHO HE REALLY WAS. BECAUSE JESUS WAS TEMPTED, YOU HAVE A SAVIOR WHO NOT ONLY UNDERSTANDS WHEN YOU ARE TEMPTED, BUT ALSO PROMISES TO HELP YOU SAY NO TO TEMPTATIONS (1 CORINTHIANS 10:13), JUST AS HE DID. AND NOTICE HOW JESUS DID IT: WITH THE WORDS OF GOD. THEY'RE YOUR GUIDE, YOUR SHIELD, AND YOUR SWORD TO DEFEAT THE TRAPS OF THE EVIL ONE (EPHESIANS 6:16–17).

The First Miracles

John 2; Luke 5

JESUS AND HIS DISCIPLES WERE INVITED TO A WEDDING IN CANA IN GALILEE. JESUS' MOTHER MARY WAS THERE, TOO. EVERYONE WAS HAVING A GOOD TIME, BUT THEN THE WINE RAN OUT! MARY CAME TO TELL JESUS ABOUT THE PROBLEM.

"WHY ARE YOU TELLING ME?" HE ASKED HER. "IT ISN'T TIME FOR ME TO SHOW MYSELF."

BUT MARY QUIETLY TOLD THE SERVANT TO DO WHATEVER JESUS TOLD THEM TO DO, FOR SHE HOPED THAT HE WOULD HELP.

THERE WERE SIX HUGE STONE WATER JUGS NEARBY. JESUS TOLD THE SERVANTS TO FILL THE JARS WITH WATER, AND THEY DID SO. NEXT HE TOLD THEM TO TAKE SOME OF THIS TO THE HEAD WAITER. WHEN THE HEAD WAITER TASTED IT, HE EXCLAIMED, "NORMALLY PEOPLE BRING OUT THE BEST WINE FIRST, AND WHEN IT IS ALL GONE, THEN THEY USE THE CHEAPER WINE. BUT YOU HAVE SAVED THE BEST TILL LAST!" THE JUGS WERE NOW FILLED WITH DELICIOUS WINE.

THIS WAS THE FIRST OF MANY MIRACLES WHICH JESUS WOULD PERFORM.

SOME TIME AFTER THIS, JESUS WAS WALKING THROUGH A TOWN WHEN A MAN CAME UP TO HIM. HE WAS COVERED WITH LEPROSY. WHEN HE SAW JESUS HE FELL TO HIS KNEES, AND CRIED OUT, "LORD, IF YOU WANT TO, YOU CAN MAKE ME CLEAN."

JESUS WAS FILLED WITH COMPASSION. HE REACHED OUT AND TOUCHED THE MAN. "I DO WANT TO," HE SAID. "BE CLEAN!" IMMEDIATELY THE MAN'S SKIN WAS PERFECTLY SMOOTH AND HEALTHY.

THE GRATEFUL MAN COULDN'T KEEP WHAT HAD HAPPENED TO HIMSELF, AND VERY SOON PEOPLE CAME FROM FAR AND WIDE TO SEE JESUS IN THE HOPE THAT HE WOULD CURE THEM. IN FACT, SO MANY PEOPLE FLOCKED TO JESUS THAT HUGE CROWDS WOULD GATHER WHEREVER HE WENT.

ONCE SOME MEN BROUGHT THEIR PARALYZED FRIEND TO JESUS WHEN HE WAS STAYING IN A HOUSE IN CAPERNAUM, BUT IT WAS SO PACKED THAT THEY COULDN'T GET NEAR IT. THE DETERMINED MEN CUT A HOLE IN THE ROOF AND LOWERED THEIR FRIEND DOWN INTO THE ROOM. JESUS TOLD THE MAN THAT HIS SINS WERE FORGIVEN—AND HE STOOD UP, THANKED JESUS, AND WALKED OUT ON HIS OWN TWO FEET! PEOPLE WERE AMAZED, FOR THEY HAD NEVER SEEN ANYTHING LIKE THIS BEFORE.

COMPASSION IS MORE THAN SIMPLY SEEING SORROW OR SUFFERING, IT'S ALSO BEING MOVED TO HELP. JESUS WAS—AND IS—FILLED WITH COMPASSION FOR HIS PEOPLE. AS THE SON OF GOD, HE COULD HAVE SIMPLY SPOKEN A WORD AND HEALED THE LEPER'S WOUNDS. INSTEAD, JESUS REACHED OUT AND TOUCHED THIS MAN WHO PROBABLY HADN'T BEEN TOUCHED WITH KINDNESS IN YEARS. YES, JESUS HEALED HIS BODY, BUT THE TRUE HEALING WENT DEEPER—TO HIS HEART AND SOUL.

THAT IS WHAT JESUS WANTS TO DO FOR YOU: HEAL YOUR HEART AND SOUL.

The Sermon on the Mount

Matthew 5–7; Luke 6, 11

JESUS TRAVELED ACROSS THE REGION. HE WASN'T ALWAYS WELCOME IN THE SYNAGOGUES, SO HE WOULD OFTEN TEACH OUTSIDE IN THE OPEN AIR. ONE OF THE MOST IMPORTANT TALKS HE GAVE WAS TO A HUGE CROWD ON A MOUNTAIN NEAR CAPERNAUM, NOW KNOWN AS THE SERMON ON THE MOUNT. JESUS SPOKE ABOUT WHAT WAS TRULY IMPORTANT IN LIFE AND GAVE COMFORT AND ADVICE.

HE PROMISED THAT ALL THOSE WHO ARE POOR OR SAD OR BADLY TREATED WILL BE REWARDED IN HEAVEN. THERE THEY WILL BE COMFORTED AND KNOW GREAT JOY, AS WILL THOSE WHO ARE KIND AND GENTLE AND HUMBLE: "SO BE GLAD WHEN PEOPLE ARE MEAN TO YOU AND SAY NASTY THINGS ABOUT YOU BECAUSE OF ME—FOR A GREAT REWARD IS WAITING FOR YOU IN HEAVEN!" JESUS TOLD THEM.

JESUS SPOKE ABOUT THE IMPORTANCE OF FORGIVENESS—IT ISN'T ENOUGH JUST TO OBEY GOD'S LAWS. WE NEED TO LEARN TO TRULY FORGIVE TO BECOME CLOSE TO GOD. AND WHILE IT IS EASY TO LOVE OUR FRIENDS, HOW PLEASED WILL GOD BE IF WE CAN LEARN TO LOVE OUR ENEMIES!

"AND LET YOUR LIFE BE AN EXAMPLE TO OTHERS. BUT DON'T DO GOOD THINGS JUST SO PEOPLE WILL LOOK AT YOU AND THINK HOW GOOD YOU ARE. YOU DON'T NEED THEIR PRAISE. DO YOUR GOOD DEEDS IN PRIVATE, AND YOUR FATHER, WHO SEES EVERYTHING, WILL REWARD YOU."

JESUS TOLD THE PEOPLE THAT THEY SHOULDN'T SPEND THEIR TIME TRYING TO MAKE THEMSELVES COMFORTABLE NOW. "DON'T STORE UP WEALTH ON EARTH," HE TOLD THEM. "IT WON'T LAST! STORE UP TREASURES IN HEAVEN, FOR WHERE YOUR TREASURES ARE, YOUR HEART WILL BE TOO. AND DON'T WORRY ABOUT WHAT CLOTHES YOU'RE WEARING OR WHERE YOUR NEXT MEAL WILL COME FROM. THERE IS MORE TO LIFE THAN FOOD AND CLOTHES. TRUST IN GOD TO TAKE CARE OF YOU."

JESUS ALSO TAUGHT THE RIGHT WAY TO PRAY, NOT BY REPEATING MEANINGLESS WORDS, BUT BY SPEAKING FROM OUR HEARTS, FOR GOD KNOWS WHAT WE NEED BEFORE WE ASK HIM. WE SHOULDN'T TRY TO IMPRESS OTHERS BY PRAYING IN PUBLIC, BUT SHOULD GO TO A QUIET PLACE AND PRAY TO GOD ALONE. "KEEP ON ASKING," SAID JESUS, "AND YOU WILL RECEIVE. KEEP ON SEEKING, AND YOU WILL FIND. KEEP ON KNOCKING, AND THE DOOR WILL BE OPENED TO YOU."

JESUS CAME TO TEACH US HOW TO HONOR GOD WITH OUR LIVES. A GODLY LIFE ISN'T ABOUT ALL THE STUFF WE CAN GET FOR OURSELVES; IT'S ABOUT ALL THE THINGS WE CAN GIVE AWAY—LIKE KINDNESS, GENTLENESS, AND LOVE. THOSE ARE THE TRUE TREASURES—THE ONES THAT CANNOT BE DESTROYED OR TAKEN AWAY.

JESUS ALSO CAME TO TEACH US HOW TO TALK TO OUR FATHER—NOT WITH MINDLESS WORDS REPEATED OVER AND OVER, BUT RATHER WITH THOUGHTFUL WORDS FROM A SEEKING HEART. THOSE ARE THE PRAYERS GOD PROMISES TO HEAR AND ANSWER (PSALM 91:15, ISAIAH 65:24, 1 JOHN 5:14–15).

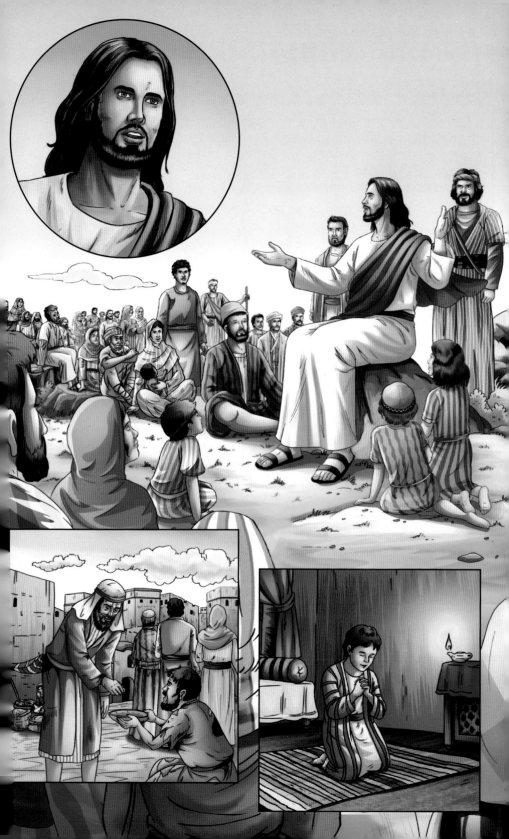

Teaching in Parables

Matthew 13; Luke 8

MANY OF THE PEOPLE WHO CAME TO LISTEN TO JESUS WERE FARMERS. JESUS TRIED TO PASS ON HIS MESSAGE IN A WAY THAT THEY WOULD UNDERSTAND. HIS STORIES, OFTEN CALLED PARABLES, LET PEOPLE THINK THINGS THROUGH FOR THEMSELVES. TO SOME THEY WOULD JUST BE STORIES, BUT OTHERS WOULD UNDERSTAND THE REAL MESSAGE.

"A FARMER WENT OUT TO SOW HIS SEED. SOME FELL ALONG THE PATH AND WAS TRAMPLED, OR EATEN BY BIRDS. SOME FELL ON ROCKY GROUND, AND WHEN THEY BEGAN TO GROW, THE PLANTS WITHERED BECAUSE THEIR ROOTS COULD NOT REACH WATER. OTHER SEEDS FELL AMONG WEEDS WHICH CHOKED THEM. STILL OTHERS FELL ON GOOD SOIL AND GREW INTO TALL, STRONG PLANTS AND PRODUCED A CROP FAR GREATER THAN WHAT WAS SOWN."

JESUS WAS TELLING THEM THAT HE WAS LIKE THE FARMER, AND THE SEEDS LIKE THE MESSAGE HE BROUGHT FROM GOD. THOSE THAT WERE EATEN ARE LIKE PEOPLE WHO HEAR THE GOOD NEWS BUT PAY NO ATTENTION. THOSE ON THE ROCKY GROUND ARE LIKE PEOPLE WHO RECEIVE THE WORD WITH JOY, BUT HAVE NO ROOTS—WHEN LIFE GETS DIFFICULT THEY GIVE UP. THE SEEDS AMONG WEEDS ARE LIKE THOSE WHO HEAR BUT LET THEMSELVES BECOME CHOKED BY LIFE'S WORRIES AND PLEASURES. BUT THE SEEDS THAT FELL ON GOOD SOIL ARE LIKE THOSE WHO HEAR GOD'S MESSAGE AND HOLD IT TIGHT IN THEIR HEART. THEIR FAITH GROWS AND GROWS.

JESUS TOLD ANOTHER PARABLE: "ONCE A FARMER SOWED GOOD SEED IN HIS FIELD, BUT THAT NIGHT, HIS ENEMY SOWED WEEDS AMONG THE WHEAT. WHEN THE WHEAT BEGAN TO GROW, WEEDS GREW TOO. HIS SERVANTS ASKED IF THEY SHOULD PULL THEM UP, BUT THE OWNER SAID THAT THEN THEY MIGHT PULL SOME OF THE WHEAT UP BY MISTAKE. 'WE MUST LET BOTH GROW UNTIL HARVEST,' HE SAID. 'THEN WE WILL COLLECT AND BURN THE WEEDS, AND GATHER THE WHEAT, AND STORE IT SAFELY.'"

JESUS LATER EXPLAINED, "THE FARMER WHO SOWED THE GOOD SEED IS THE SON OF MAN. THE SEED IS HIS PEOPLE. THE WEEDS WERE SOWN BY THE DEVIL, AND THEY ARE HIS PEOPLE. THE HARVEST WILL COME AT THE END OF TIME. THEN THE SON OF MAN WILL SEND OUT HIS ANGELS, TO WEED OUT OF HIS KINGDOM EVERYTHING THAT CAUSES SIN AND ALL WHO DO EVIL, AND THROW THEM INTO THE BLAZING FURNACE. BUT THE RIGHTEOUS WILL SHINE LIKE THE SUN IN THE KINGDOM OF THEIR FATHER."

IF YOUR HEART IS LIKE THE SOIL IN JESUS' PARABLE, WHAT KIND OF SOIL IS IT? IS IT SO HARD THAT HIS WORD CANNOT TOUCH IT? WHEN THINGS GET TOUGH, DO YOU GIVE UP ON GOD? ARE WORRIES—OR PLEASURES—CHOKING OUT YOUR FAITH?

THE GOOD NEWS IS THAT GOD CAN CHANGE YOUR HEART. JUST ASK! ASK HIM TO SOFTEN YOUR HEART (EZEKIEL 36:26), TO GIVE YOU EARS TO TRULY HEAR HIS WORD, A MIND TO UNDERSTAND IT, AND A HEART TO LOVE IT. THAT'S A PRAYER HE PROMISES TO ANSWER (JEREMIAH 29:13).

Jesus the Storyteller

ONCE SOMEONE ASKED JESUS WHAT THE LAW MEANT WHEN IT SAID WE MUST LOVE OUR NEIGHBORS AS MUCH AS OURSELVES. "WHO IS MY NEIGHBOR?" HE ASKED, AND JESUS TOLD HIM A STORY:

"A MAN WAS GOING FROM JERUSALEM TO JERICHO, WHEN HE WAS ATTACKED BY ROBBERS WHO BEAT HIM, STOLE ALL HIS THINGS, AND LEFT HIM BY THE ROADSIDE, HALF DEAD. SOON A PRIEST PASSED BY, AND THEN A LEVITE CAME ALONG. BOTH AVOIDED THE MAN AND HURRIED ON THEIR WAY.

"NEXT CAME A SAMARITAN, AN ENEMY OF THE JEWS. YET WHEN HE SAW THE MAN LYING BY THE ROADSIDE, HE WAS FILLED WITH PITY. HE WASHED AND BANDAGED HIS WOUNDS, AND TOOK HIM TO AN INN, WHERE HE PAID FOR HIM TO BE LOOKED AFTER."

JESUS LOOKED AT THE MAN WHO HAD POSED THE QUESTION, AND ASKED WHO HAD BEEN A GOOD NEIGHBOR TO THE INJURED MAN. THE MAN SHEEPISHLY REPLIED, "THE ONE WHO WAS KIND TO HIM."

THEN JESUS TOLD HIM, "GO, THEN, AND BE LIKE HIM."

JESUS TOLD ANOTHER STORY TO EXPLAIN HOW HAPPY GOD WAS WHEN SINNERS RETURNED TO HIM: "THERE WAS ONCE A MAN WITH TWO SONS. THE YOUNGER ONE ASKED FOR HIS SHARE OF THE PROPERTY SO HE COULD GO OUT INTO THE WORLD, AND HE SOON SPENT IT ALL ON ENJOYING HIMSELF. HE ENDED UP WORKING FOR A FARMER AND WAS SO HUNGRY THAT SOMETIMES HE WISHED HE COULD EAT THE FOOD HE WAS GIVING TO THE PIGS! BUT AT LAST HE CAME TO HIS SENSES AND SET OFF HOME TO TELL HIS FATHER HOW SORRY HE WAS. "I'M NOT WORTHY OF BEING HIS SON," HE THOUGHT, "BUT MAYBE HE WILL LET ME WORK ON THE FARM."

"WHEN HIS FATHER SAW HIM COMING, HE RUSHED OUT AND THREW HIS ARMS AROUND HIM. THE YOUNG MAN TRIED TO TELL HIM THAT HE WAS NOT FIT TO BE CALLED HIS SON, BUT THE FATHER TOLD HIS SERVANTS TO BRING HIS FINEST ROBE FOR HIS SON TO WEAR AND TO KILL THE PRIZE CALF FOR A FEAST.

"THE OLDER SON THOUGHT THIS UNFAIR! BUT HIS FATHER TOLD HIM, 'SON, YOU ARE ALWAYS WITH ME, AND ALL I HAVE IS YOURS. BUT CELEBRATE WITH ME NOW, FOR YOUR BROTHER WAS DEAD TO ME AND IS ALIVE AGAIN; HE WAS LOST AND IS FOUND!'"

"WHEN HIS FATHER SAW HIM COMING . . ." DID YOU NOTICE THAT LINE? THE FATHER WAS LOOKING FOR HIS CHILD—EVEN THOUGH HE'D RUN AWAY, EVEN THOUGH HE'D DONE TERRIBLE THINGS, EVEN THOUGH IT HAD BEEN A LONG TIME.

GOD IS LIKE THAT FATHER. YES, HE KNOWS ALL YOU'VE DONE—THE GOOD, THE TERRIBLE, THE SHAMEFUL. YET HE'S STILL LOOKING FOR YOU TO COME HOME TO HIM. YOU DON'T HAVE TO HAVE IT ALL FIXED OR FIGURED OUT. YOU JUST HAVE TO TAKE THAT FIRST STEP TOWARD HIM. AND WHEN YOU DO . . . YOUR FATHER COMES RUSHING OUT TO YOU.

The Miracle Worker

Matthew 8–9; Mark 4; Luke 8

JESUS AND HIS DISCIPLES CLIMBED INTO A BOAT TO TRAVEL ACROSS TO THE OTHER SIDE OF THE LAKE. JESUS WAS SO TIRED THAT HE LAY DOWN AND FELL ASLEEP. SUDDENLY, THE SKIES DARKENED, RAIN CAME PELTING DOWN, AND A FIERCE STORM STRUCK THE LAKE. HUGE WAVES TOSSED THE BOAT, AND THE DISCIPLES WERE TERRIFIED THAT THEY WOULD CAPSIZE.

JESUS LAY SLEEPING. THE FRIGHTENED DISCIPLES WOKE HIM UP, BEGGING HIM TO SAVE THEM. JESUS OPENED HIS EYES AND LOOKED UP AT THEM. "WHY ARE YOU AFRAID? YOU HAVE SO LITTLE FAITH!" HE SAID, SADLY. THEN HE STOOD UP CALMLY, ARMS SPREAD WIDE, AND FACING INTO THE WIND AND RAIN, COMMANDED, "BE STILL!" AT ONCE THE WIND AND WAVES DIED DOWN AND ALL WAS CALM.

THE DISCIPLES WERE AMAZED. "WHO IS THIS MAN?" THEY ASKED THEMSELVES. "EVEN THE WINDS AND WAVES OBEY HIM!"

ON ANOTHER OCCASION JESUS WAS WALKING THROUGH A BUSY CROWD, TRYING TO REACH THE HOME OF JAIRUS, WHOSE YOUNG DAUGHTER WAS DREADFULLY ILL. PEOPLE CROWDED ROUND, THEN JESUS STOPPED STILL AND ASKED WHO HAD TOUCHED HIM. A WOMAN STEPPED FORWARD AND KNELT AT HIS FEET. "LORD, IT WAS ME," SHE SAID NERVOUSLY. FOR YEARS SHE HAD BEEN ILL AND NOBODY HAD BEEN ABLE TO HELP HER. BUT SHE HAD KNOWN THAT IF SHE COULD JUST GET CLOSE TO JESUS, SHE WOULD BE HEALED, AND SURE ENOUGH, THE MOMENT SHE HAD MANAGED TO TOUCH THE EDGE OF HIS CLOAK, SHE WAS WELL!

JESUS WASN'T ANGRY. "YOUR FAITH HAS HEALED YOU," HE SAID KINDLY. "GO HOME."

JUST THEN, SOMEONE CAME RUNNING UP TO SAY THAT JAIRUS'S DAUGHTER WAS DEAD! JAIRUS WAS HEARTBROKEN, BUT JESUS CARRIED ON WALKING. "TRUST ME, JAIRUS," HE SAID. "DON'T BE AFRAID."

HE ARRIVED AT THE HOUSE TO THE SOUND OF WEEPING. "WHY ARE YOU CRYING?" HE ASKED. "THE GIRL IS NOT DEAD; SHE IS JUST SLEEPING." THE PEOPLE THERE SHOOK THEIR HEADS, BUT JESUS IGNORED THEM AND WENT TO HER ROOM, WHERE HE TOOK ONE OF HER HANDS IN HIS OWN, AND WHISPERED, "WAKE UP, MY CHILD!"

IN THAT INSTANT, THE CHILD OPENED HER EYES. SHE SMILED AT JESUS AND HUGGED HER OVERJOYED PARENTS!

JESUS WASN'T JUST A GOOD MAN, A WISE TEACHER, OR A PROPHET. ONLY THE SON OF GOD COULD DO THE THINGS JESUS DID: STOP THE STORMS, HEAL THE SICK, EVEN RAISE THE DEAD TO LIFE AGAIN. JUST IMAGINE WHAT HE COULD DO IN YOUR LIFE.

WHEN JESUS IS WITH YOU IN THIS "BOAT OF LIFE," HE CAN STOP THE STORMS OF FEAR AND WORRY WITH HIS WORDS OF PEACE AND STRENGTH. HE CAN HEAL A BROKEN HEART AND A SOUL WOUNDED BY SIN. AND HE CAN RAISE YOU UP TO A NEW LIFE—ONE LIVED WITH HIM FOREVER AT YOUR SIDE (2 CORINTHIANS 5:17–19).

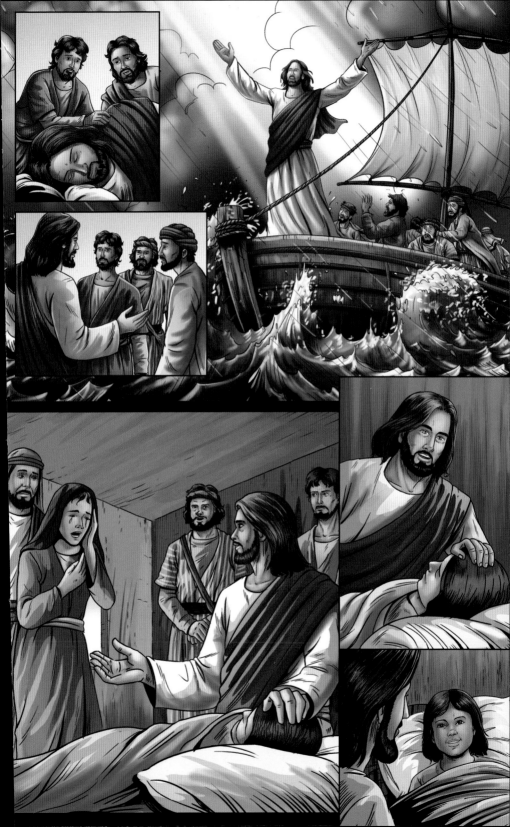

Food and Water

Matthew 14; Mark 6; Luke 9; John 6

MANY THOUSANDS OF PEOPLE HAD COME TO HEAR JESUS TALK ONE DAY, OUT ON THE HILLS ABOVE LAKE GALILEE. WHEN EVENING CAME, THERE WAS STILL A HUGE CROWD. JESUS TOLD HIS DISCIPLES TO GIVE THEM SOMETHING TO EAT. "BUT MASTER," THE DISCIPLES SAID, "THERE ARE THOUSANDS OF PEOPLE AND WE ONLY HAVE FIVE LOAVES OF BREAD AND TWO FISH!"

JESUS COMMANDED THEM TO TELL THE PEOPLE TO SIT DOWN, THEN, TAKING THE FIVE LOAVES AND THE TWO FISH AND LOOKING UP TO HEAVEN, HE GAVE THANKS TO HIS FATHER AND BROKE THE LOAVES INTO PIECES. HE GAVE THEM TO THE DISCIPLES, WHO TOOK THEM TO THE PEOPLE AND THEN CAME BACK TO JESUS FOR MORE BREAD AND FISH. HE FILLED UP THEIR BASKETS AGAIN . . . AND AGAIN . . . AND AGAIN! TO THEIR ASTONISHMENT THERE WAS STILL BREAD AND FISH LEFT IN THE BASKETS WHEN THEY CAME TO FEED THE VERY LAST PEOPLE! MORE THAN FIVE THOUSAND PEOPLE HAD BEEN FED THAT DAY—WITH FIVE LOAVES OF BREAD AND TWO FISH!

IT WAS LATER THAT SAME NIGHT AND THE DISCIPLES WERE IN A BOAT ON LAKE GALILEE. WAVES TOSSED THE BOAT VIOLENTLY. JESUS HAD GONE ASHORE TO PRAY AND THE DISCIPLES WERE AFRAID. AT THE FIRST LIGHT OF DAWN, THEY SAW A FIGURE WALKING TOWARDS THEM ON THE WATER! THEY THOUGHT IT WAS A GHOST AND WERE SCARED UNTIL THEY HEARD THE CALM VOICE OF JESUS, "IT IS I. DON'T BE AFRAID."

SIMON PETER WAS THE FIRST TO SPEAK. "LORD," HE SAID, "IF IT IS YOU, COMMAND ME TO WALK ACROSS THE WATER TO YOU," AND JESUS DID SO.

HE PUT ONE FOOT GINGERLY IN THE WATER. THEN HE LOWERED THE OTHER, AND BRAVELY STOOD UP, LETTING GO OF THE BOAT. HE DIDN'T SINK! BUT WHEN HE LOOKED AROUND AT THE WAVES, HIS COURAGE FAILED HIM. AS HE BEGAN TO SINK, HE CRIED, "LORD, SAVE ME!"

JESUS REACHED OUT AND TOOK HIS HAND. "OH, PETER," HE SAID SADLY, "WHERE IS YOUR FAITH? WHY DID YOU DOUBT?" THEN TOGETHER THEY WALKED BACK TO THE BOAT. THE WIND DIED DOWN AND THE WATER BECAME CALM. THE DISCIPLES BOWED LOW. "TRULY YOU ARE THE SON OF GOD," THEY SAID HUMBLY.

IT'S EASY TO LOOK AT THESE EVENTS FROM THE BIBLE AND SEE THE OBVIOUS: THE DISCIPLES WHO DIDN'T KNOW HOW TO FEED A CROWD, THE BASKETS OF LEFTOVER FISH AND BREAD, PETER WALKING ON THE WATER . . . AND THEN SINKING UNDER WAVES.

LOOK AT JESUS INSTEAD. WHAT'S HE DOING? HE'S GIVING HUNGRY PEOPLE WHAT THEY NEED. HE'S WALKING THROUGH A STORM TO HELP THOSE STUCK IN THAT STORM. HE'S REACHING OUT TO SAVE THE ONE WHO'S CALLING OUT TO HIM. JESUS WANTS TO DO ALL THOSE THINGS FOR YOU TOO—PROVIDE, HELP, SAVE. HE'S WAITING FOR YOU TO REACH OUT TO HIM.

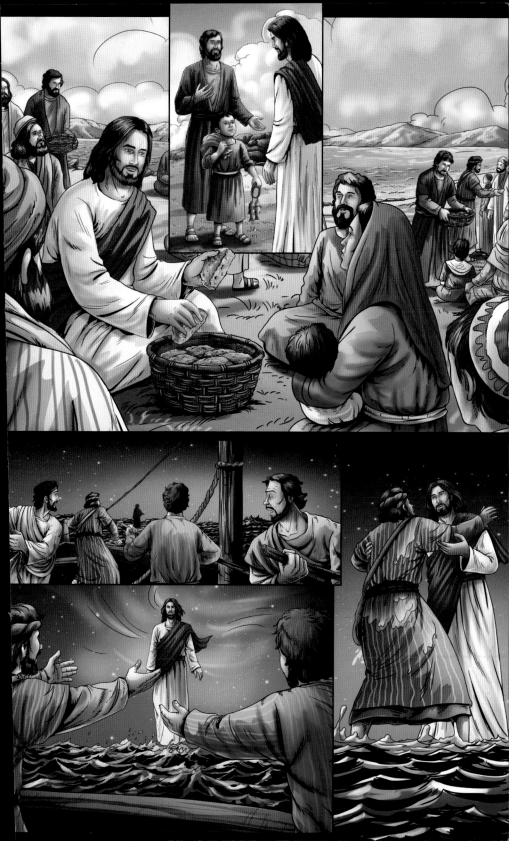

Jesus Comes to Jerusalem

Matthew 21, 26; Mark 11, 14; Luke 19, 22; John 12

JERUSALEM WAS PACKED. IT WAS THE WEEK OF THE PASSOVER FESTIVAL, AND EVERYONE HAD GATHERED TO CELEBRATE. JESUS ENTERED JERUSALEM RIDING A DONKEY. HE WAS MET BY A BIG CROWD, FOR MANY HAD HEARD OF THE MIRACLES HE HAD PERFORMED. SOME OF THE RELIGIOUS LEADERS FEARED AND HATED JESUS, BUT MANY OF THE PEOPLE TRULY SAW HIM AS THEIR KING, AND THEY TRIED TO GIVE HIM A KING'S WELCOME, CALLING OUT, "HOSANNA TO THE SON OF DAVID!"

BUT JESUS WAS SAD, FOR HE KNEW THAT IN A VERY SHORT TIME THESE PEOPLE CHEERING HIM WOULD TURN AGAINST HIM.

THE FIRST THING JESUS DID IN JERUSALEM WAS TO VISIT HIS FATHER'S TEMPLE. IT WAS FULL OF MONEY LENDERS AND PEOPLE SELLING ANIMALS, TRYING TO MAKE MONEY OUT OF THOSE WHO CAME TO MAKE SACRIFICES TO GOD. JESUS WAS ANGRY. "NO!" HE SHOUTED. "GOD SAID THAT THIS TEMPLE WAS TO BE A PLACE WHERE PEOPLE FROM ALL NATIONS COULD COME TO PRAY TO HIM. YOU HAVE MADE IT A DEN OF ROBBERS!" AND HE THREW EVERYONE OUT WHO SHOULDN'T BE THERE.

WHEN THE TEMPLE WAS ONCE AGAIN CALM, THE POOR PEOPLE, THE BEGGARS, AND THE SICK BEGAN TO FIND THEIR WAY BACK IN, AND CAME TO JESUS TO BE HEALED AND TO FEEL BETTER. EVERYONE WAS HAPPY—APART FROM THE PHARISEES, WHO PLOTTED TO GET RID OF HIM.

JESUS KNEW THAT THE PHARISEES AND THOSE WHO HATED AND FEARED HIM WERE WAITING FOR ANY OPPORTUNITY TO ARREST HIM. YET EVEN AMONG HIS DEAREST FRIENDS THERE WAS ONE WHO WOULD BE HIS ENEMY . . .

JUDAS ISCARIOT, THE DISCIPLE IN CHARGE OF THE MONEY, WAS DISHONEST. HE KEPT SOME FOR HIMSELF INSTEAD OF GIVING IT TO THOSE IN NEED. HIS GREED MADE HIM DO A VERY BAD THING. JUDAS WENT TO THE CHIEF PRIESTS IN SECRET AND ASKED THEM HOW MUCH THEY WOULD GIVE HIM IF HE DELIVERED JESUS INTO THEIR HANDS.

THE PRIESTS COULDN'T BELIEVE THEIR EARS! THEY KNEW THAT JUDAS WAS ONE OF JESUS' CLOSEST FRIENDS. THEY OFFERED HIM THIRTY PIECES OF SILVER . . . AND JUDAS ACCEPTED! FROM THEN ON, JUDAS WAS SIMPLY WAITING FOR THE OPPORTUNITY TO HAND JESUS OVER.

THE FIRST THING JESUS DID WHEN HE ENTERED JERUSALEM WAS GO TO HIS FATHER'S HOUSE. JESUS KNEW THAT—IN SPITE OF THE CHEERING CROWDS—HE WAS HATED AND FEARED BY MANY. HE KNEW JUDAS WOULD SOON SELL HIM OUT FOR THIRTY PIECES OF SILVER. AND HE KNEW THE CROSS AND ALL ITS SUFFERING WAS COMING. SO WHAT DID JESUS DO? HE WENT TO HIS FATHER'S HOUSE TO BE ABOUT HIS FATHER'S BUSINESS.

AND THAT'S WHAT HE ASKS OF YOU. BE ABOUT THE FATHER'S BUSINESS. LOVE AND HONOR HIM. LOVE AND SERVE OTHERS. AFTER ALL, THAT'S WHAT JESUS DID.

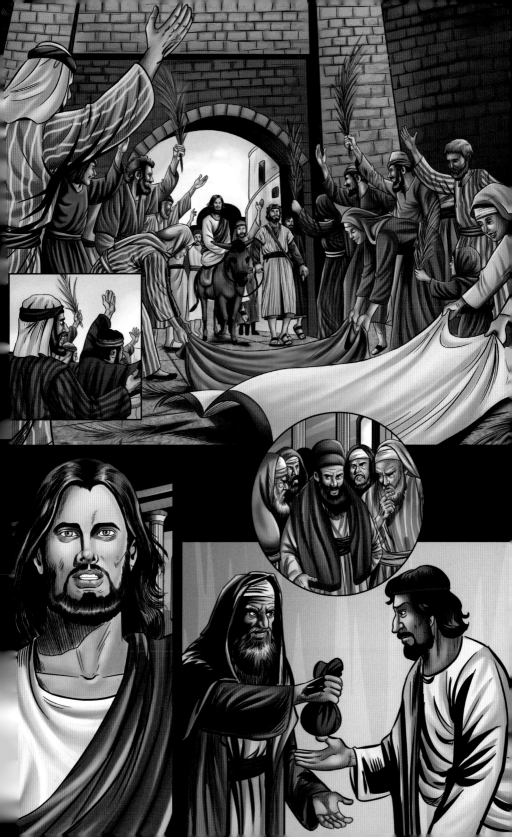

The Last Supper

Matthew 26; Mark 14; Luke 22; John 13–15

IT WAS NEARLY TIME FOR THE PASSOVER FEAST, AND A KIND MAN HAD SET ASIDE A ROOM FOR THE DISCIPLES TO PREPARE FOR IT. THAT NIGHT, WHEN THEY WERE EATING, JESUS BEGAN TO WASH AND DRY THE DISCIPLES' FEET LIKE A SERVANT. SIMON PETER PROTESTED IN HORROR, "LORD, YOU MUSTN'T WASH MY FEET!"

JESUS REPLIED GENTLY, "YOU DON'T UNDERSTAND WHAT I'M DOING, BUT LATER IT WILL BE CLEAR TO YOU. UNLESS I WASH YOU, YOU WON'T REALLY BELONG TO ME." HE HAD WASHED THEIR FEET LIKE A SERVANT, SO THAT THEY COULD LEARN TO DO THE SAME FOR ONE ANOTHER.

JESUS KNEW HE WOULD SOON HAVE TO LEAVE HIS FRIENDS. HE WAS SAD AND TROUBLED. "SOON, ONE OF YOU WILL BETRAY ME," HE SAID SORROWFULLY. THE DISCIPLES LOOKED AT ONE ANOTHER IN SHOCK. WHO COULD HE MEAN?

"HE WHO DIPS HIS BREAD WITH MINE IS THE ONE," SAID JESUS, AND WHEN JUDAS ISCARIOT DIPPED HIS BREAD INTO THE SAME BOWL, JESUS SAID SOFTLY, "GO AND DO WHAT YOU HAVE TO DO." JUDAS LEFT, BUT THE OTHERS DIDN'T UNDERSTAND.

THEN JESUS HANDED AROUND SOME BREAD, SAYING, "THIS IS MY BODY, WHICH WILL BE BROKEN." NEXT, HE PASSED AROUND A CUP OF WINE, SAYING, "DRINK THIS. IT IS MY BLOOD, WHICH WILL TAKE AWAY SIN," AND HE TOLD THEM HE WOULD SOON BE LEAVING THEM.

SIMON PETER CRIED OUT, "BUT LORD, WHERE ARE YOU GOING? WHY CAN'T I FOLLOW YOU? I WOULD READILY LAY DOWN MY LIFE FOR YOU!"

"WOULD YOU, MY FRIEND?" ASKED JESUS GENTLY. "AND YET YOU WILL DISOWN ME THREE TIMES BEFORE THE COCK CROWS!" PETER WAS HORRIFIED. HE FELT THIS COULD NEVER HAPPEN.

JESUS TRIED TO COMFORT THE DISCIPLES, SAYING THAT HE WAS GOING AHEAD TO PREPARE A PLACE FOR THEM IN HIS FATHER'S HOUSE. THEY WOULD KNOW HOW TO FIND THEIR WAY THERE, HE SAID, FOR "THE ONLY WAY TO THE FATHER IS THROUGH BELIEVING IN ME. IF YOU REALLY KNOW ME, YOU WILL KNOW MY FATHER AS WELL."

HE GAVE THEM THIS COMMAND: "LOVE ONE ANOTHER, AS I HAVE LOVED EACH OF YOU. THERE IS NO GREATER LOVE THAN TO LAY DOWN ONE'S LIFE FOR ONE'S FRIENDS."

JESUS WAS ABOUT TO DIE, BUT HE DIDN'T SNAP HIS FINGERS AND DEMAND TO BE SERVED. INSTEAD, HE SERVED. JESUS KNELT TO WASH THE DIRTY FEET THAT SOON RAN AWAY FROM HIM. HE PRAYED FOR PETER WHO WOULD LATER PRETEND HE DIDN'T EVEN KNOW HIM. AND HE SHARED BREAD WITH JUDAS WHO WAS JUST WAITING TO BETRAY HIM. JESUS SERVED, BECAUSE THAT'S WHAT HE CAME TO DO (MATTHEW 20:28).

AND HE'S STILL SERVING, PREPARING A PLACE FOR YOU IN HIS FATHER'S HOME. THERE'S PLENTY OF ROOM. FOLLOW HIM. BECAUSE THE ONLY WAY TO GOD AND HEAVEN IS THROUGH HIM.

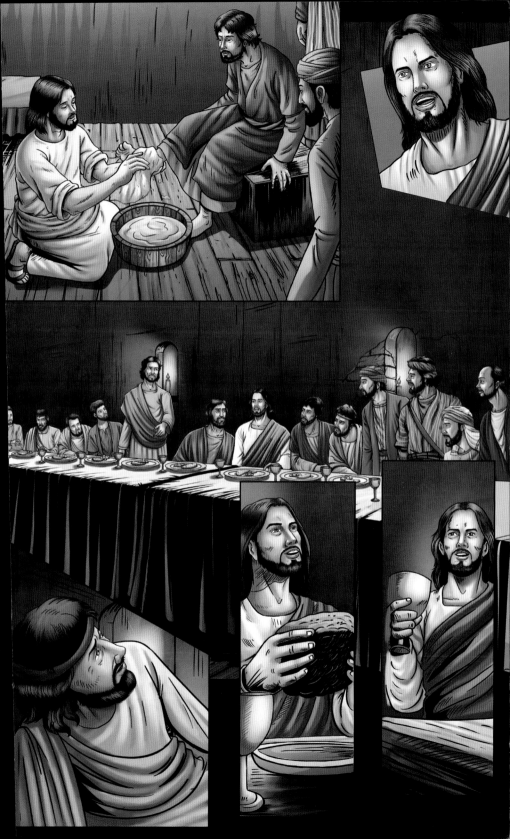

Betrayal

JESUS AND THE DISCIPLES LEFT THE CITY TO GO TO A QUIET GARDEN CALLED GETHSEMANE. JESUS PRAYED TO HIS FATHER FOR HIS DISCIPLES, AND FOR ALL THOSE WHO WOULD COME TO BELIEVE IN HIM BECAUSE OF THE MESSAGE THEY WOULD SPREAD THROUGHOUT THE WORLD.

THEN JESUS WENT TO ONE SIDE, BUT HE TOOK PETER, JAMES, AND JOHN WITH HIM, ASKING THEM TO KEEP HIM COMPANY. HE WENT AWAY FROM THEM TO PRAY IN PRIVATE.

"FATHER," HE CRIED OUT IN ANGUISH, "IF IT IS POSSIBLE, MAY I NOT HAVE TO GO THROUGH THIS!" YET HIS VERY NEXT WORDS WERE, "YET LET IT NOT BE AS I WILL, BUT AS YOU WILL, FATHER," FOR JESUS KNEW THAT GOD WASN'T MAKING HIM DO ANYTHING: HE HAD CHOSEN FREELY TO DO IT.

WHEN HE RETURNED TO HIS FRIENDS, THEY WERE SLEEPING. "COULDN'T YOU KEEP WATCH WITH ME FOR JUST ONE HOUR?" HE SIGHED. HE WENT AGAIN TO TALK TO HIS FATHER, BUT WHEN HE RETURNED, THE DISCIPLES WERE FAST ASLEEP AGAIN. THIS HAPPENED ONCE MORE, AND THIS TIME WHEN HE WOKE THEM, HE SAID, "THE HOUR HAS COME. YOU NEED TO GET UP, FOR THE ONE WHO HAS BETRAYED ME IS HERE!"

A CROWD OF PEOPLE BURST INTO THE GARDEN, MANY ARMED WITH WEAPONS. AT THE HEAD OF THEM WAS JUDAS ISCARIOT. HE HAD TOLD THE CHIEF PRIESTS THAT HE WOULD KISS JESUS SO THAT THEY WOULD KNOW WHOM TO ARREST. AS JUDAS APPROACHED HIM, JESUS SAID SADLY, "OH JUDAS, WOULD YOU BETRAY THE SON OF MAN WITH A KISS?"

PETER DREW HIS SWORD, BUT JESUS TOLD HIM TO PUT HIS SWORD AWAY, AND HE ALLOWED THE SOLDIERS TO ARREST HIM. "I'M THE ONE YOU HAVE COME TO FIND," HE SAID QUIETLY. "LET THESE OTHERS GO. YOU HAD NO NEED TO COME HERE WITH SWORDS AND CLUBS. YOU COULD EASILY HAVE TAKEN ME WHEN I WAS IN THE TEMPLE COURTS."

WHEN THE DISCIPLES REALIZED THAT JESUS WAS GOING TO ALLOW HIMSELF TO BE TAKEN PRISONER, THEY FLED IN FEAR AND DESPAIR.

JESUS COULD HAVE SAID NO.

IN THAT GARDEN, JESUS COULD HAVE SAID, "NO, I WON'T DO THIS." INSTEAD HE PRAYED, "AS YOU WILL, FATHER." WHEN JUDAS BETRAYED HIM WITH A KISS, JESUS COULD HAVE STOPPED HIM WITH A WORD. BUT HE DIDN'T. AND WHEN THE CROWDS CAME WITH THEIR TORCHES AND THEIR SWORDS, JESUS COULD HAVE CALLED DOWN AN ARMY OF HEAVEN'S ANGELS TO STOP THEM (MATTHEW 26:53), YET HE QUIETLY SURRENDERED.

WHY? WHY DID THE SON OF GOD ALLOW HIMSELF TO BE BETRAYED, ABANDONED AND ARRESTED? TO SAVE YOU.

Passed Around

Matthew 26–27; Mark 14–15; Luke 22–23; John 18

WHEN THE SOLDIERS TOOK JESUS TO BE QUESTIONED, SIMON PETER FOLLOWED THEM TO THE COURTYARD OF THE HIGH PRIEST. HE WAITED OUTSIDE MISERABLY, ALONG WITH THE GUARDS, WARMING THEMSELVES AT THE FIRE. AS ONE OF THE SERVANT GIRLS WAS WALKING BY, SHE CAUGHT SIGHT OF PETER. "WEREN'T YOU WITH JESUS OF NAZARETH?" SHE ASKED HIM. "I'M SURE I SAW YOU WITH HIM."

"NO, YOU'VE GOT THE WRONG MAN!" PETER HISSED QUIETLY, FOR HE FEARED WHAT WOULD HAPPEN IF THE GUARDS BELIEVED HE WAS ONE OF JESUS' DISCIPLES.

THE GIRL SHRUGGED AND WALKED AWAY, BUT ON HER WAY BACK, SHE SAID TO ONE OF THE GUARDS, "DON'T YOU THINK HE LOOKS LIKE ONE OF JESUS' FOLLOWERS?"

"I DON'T HAVE ANYTHING TO DO WITH HIM!" PANICKED PETER.

NOW THE OTHER GUARDS WERE LOOKING AT HIM. "YOU MUST BE ONE OF THEM," SAID ONE. "I CAN TELL FROM YOUR ACCENT YOU'RE FROM GALILEE."

"I SWEAR I'VE NEVER EVEN MET HIM!" CRIED PETER, HIS HEART RACING.

AT THAT VERY MOMENT, A COCK CROWED. PETER REMEMBERED WHAT JESUS HAD SAID, AND HE BROKE DOWN AND WEPT IN DISMAY.

THE PRIESTS AND PHARISEES QUESTIONED JESUS. THEY ASKED HIM IF HE WAS THE MESSIAH, THE SON OF GOD. JESUS REPLIED, "YOU HAVE SAID SO. BUT FROM NOW ON YOU WILL SEE THE SON OF MAN SITTING AT THE RIGHT HAND OF GOD."

THEY WERE FURIOUS, BUT ONLY THE ROMAN GOVERNOR, PONTIUS PILATE, COULD ORDER HIS DEATH. SO THEY DRAGGED HIM BEFORE PILATE, BUT ALTHOUGH PILATE ASKED JESUS MANY QUESTIONS, HE COULD FIND NO REASON TO PUT HIM TO DEATH. "BUT HE'S A TROUBLEMAKER!" THE PRIESTS COMPLAINED. "HE STARTED IN GALILEE AND MADE HIS WAY HERE!"

NOW PILATE SAW A WAY OF GETTING RID OF THE PROBLEM, FOR HEROD WAS IN CHARGE OF GALILEE. SO JESUS WAS TAKEN BEFORE HEROD. BUT HOWEVER MANY QUESTIONS HEROD ASKED, JESUS REMAINED GRAVE AND SILENT. IN THE END, HEROD GREW TIRED OF HIS SILENCE. THEN HE AND HIS SOLDIERS MADE FUN OF JESUS, BEFORE SENDING HIM BACK TO PILATE.

PETER KNEW THAT JESUS WAS THE SON OF GOD (MATTHEW 16:16). BUT ON THAT DARK NIGHT, FEAR HAD HIM SAYING NOT ONCE, BUT THREE TIMES, "I DON'T KNOW THE MAN!"

DOES FEAR HAVE YOU SAYING, "I DON'T KNOW HIM"? A FEAR OF WHAT OTHERS WILL THINK OF YOU? OR PERHAPS IT'S A FEAR OF WHAT HE WILL THINK OF YOU? WHAT WILL JESUS DO IF YOU GO TO HIM WITH ALL YOUR SINS AND MISTAKES? DON'T LET FEAR KEEP YOU AWAY FROM THE SAVIOR. BECAUSE HIS WORDS ARE THE ONLY ONES THAT MATTER, AND YOU CAN BE CERTAIN HE'LL SAY, "WELCOME, FRIEND" (JOHN 15:15).

The Crucifixion

Matthew 27; Mark 15; Luke 23; John 18–19

PILATE WAS UNDER PRESSURE TO ORDER THE EXECUTION OF JESUS, BUT THERE WAS ONE POSSIBLE WAY OUT. DURING PASSOVER IT WAS THE CUSTOM TO RELEASE ONE PRISONER. PILATE ASKED THE CROWD WHOM HE SHOULD RELEASE, BUT INSTEAD OF CALLING FOR JESUS, THEY CALLED FOR THE RELEASE OF A MAN NAMED BARABBAS, AND THEY SHOUTED FOR JESUS TO BE CRUCIFIED.

PILATE DIDN'T WANT TO ORDER THE EXECUTION–BUT NEITHER DID HE WANT A RIOT! HE SENT FOR A BOWL OF WATER AND WASHED HIS HANDS IN IT TO SHOW THAT HE TOOK NO RESPONSIBILITY FOR JESUS' DEATH.

THEN JESUS WAS TAKEN AWAY BY SOLDIERS. THEY MOCKED HIM, DRESSED HIM IN A PURPLE ROBE, AND PUT A CROWN OF THORNY BRANCHES ON HIS HEAD. THEN THEY BEAT HIM, BEFORE LEADING HIM THROUGH THE STREETS TO THE HILL OF GOLGOTHA.

THEY MADE HIM CARRY THE HEAVY WOODEN CROSS ON HIS BACK. WHEN HE COULD CARRY IT NO LONGER–FOR HE HAD BEEN DREADFULLY BEATEN–THEY SNATCHED SOMEONE FROM OUT OF THE CROWD TO CARRY IT FOR HIM.

AT GOLGOTHA, SOLDIERS NAILED JESUS' HANDS AND FEET TO THE CROSS AND PLACED ABOVE HIS HEAD A SIGN SAYING, 'JESUS OF NAZARETH, KING OF THE JEWS'. AS THEY RAISED THE CROSS, JESUS CRIED, "FATHER, FORGIVE THEM. THEY DON'T KNOW WHAT THEY'RE DOING."

TWO THIEVES WERE CRUCIFIED BESIDE HIM. THE FIRST SNEERED AT HIM, BUT THE OTHER SAID, "BE QUIET! WE DESERVE OUR PUNISHMENT, BUT THIS MAN HAS DONE NOTHING WRONG." HE ASKED JESUS TO REMEMBER HIM WHEN HE CAME INTO HIS KINGDOM, AND JESUS PROMISED HE WOULD BE WITH HIM THAT DAY IN PARADISE.

AT MIDDAY, A SHADOW PASSED ACROSS THE SUN AND DARKNESS FELL OVER THE LAND. AT THREE O'CLOCK IN THE AFTERNOON, JESUS CRIED OUT IN A LOUD VOICE, "MY GOD, WHY HAVE YOU FORSAKEN ME?" THEN HE GAVE A GREAT CRY, "IT IS FINISHED!" AND WITH THESE WORDS, HE GAVE UP HIS SPIRIT.

AT THAT MOMENT THE EARTH SHOOK, AND THE CURTAIN IN THE HOLY TEMPLE WAS TORN FROM TOP TO BOTTOM. THE SOLDIERS LOOKED AT ONE ANOTHING IN SHOCK. "SURELY HE WAS THE SON OF GOD!" WHISPERED ONE IN AMAZEMENT.

JESUS CAME TO THIS EARTH AND LIVED A PERFECT LIFE–SO THAT HE COULD DIE AS THE PERFECT SACRIFICE.

WE ARE THE SIN-FILLED ONES WHO DESERVE TO BE PUNISHED. NOT THE INNOCENT SON OF GOD WHO CAME ONLY TO LOVE AND SERVE. JESUS TOOK OUR PLACE ON THE CROSS. EVERY SIN WAS PLACED ON HIM, AND HE BORE THE PUNISHMENT FOR THEM SO THAT WE WOULD NEVER HAVE TO. BY HIS WOUNDS YOU ARE HEALED, AND BY HIS BLOOD YOU ARE WASHED CLEAN OF ALL YOUR SINS (1 PETER 2:24) . . . IF YOU CHOOSE TO FOLLOW HIM.

Jesus is Alive!

Matthew 27–28; Mark 15–16; Luke 23–24; John 19–20

EARLY ON THE FIRST DAY OF THE WEEK, MARY MAGDALENE AND SOME OTHER WOMEN WENT TO ANOINT THE BODY, WHICH HAD BEEN PLACED IN A TOMB, SEALED BY A LARGE STONE, AND WAS BEING GUARDED BY SOLDIERS. AS THEY CAME NEAR, THE EARTH SHOOK, THE GUARDS WERE THROWN TO THE GROUND, AND THE WOMEN SAW THAT THE STONE HAD BEEN ROLLED AWAY. AND INSIDE THE TOMB WAS AN ANGEL!

THE ANGEL SAID, "WHY ARE YOU LOOKING FOR THE LIVING AMONG THE DEAD. HE ISN'T HERE–HE HAS RISEN, JUST AS HE TOLD YOU HE WOULD!" SO THE WOMEN HURRIED AWAY TO TELL THE DISCIPLES THE NEWS, AFRAID YET FILLED WITH JOY.

LATER, MARY MAGDALENE STOOD OUTSIDE THE TOMB ALONE. SHE HEARD STEPS BEHIND HER, AND A MAN ASKED, "WHY DO YOU CRY? WHO ARE YOU LOOKING FOR?"

THINKING THIS MUST BE THE GARDENER, SHE BEGGED, "SIR, IF YOU HAVE MOVED HIM, PLEASE TELL ME WHERE HE IS." THE MAN ONLY SPOKE HER NAME, BUT THAT WAS ENOUGH. "TEACHER!" SHE GASPED, AND REACHED OUT TOWARDS JESUS.

JESUS SAID, "DON'T HOLD ON TO ME, FOR I HAVE NOT YET ASCENDED TO MY FATHER. GO AND TELL THE OTHERS!" AND SHE DID!

LATER THAT DAY, A STRANGER APPEARED TO TWO OF JESUS' FOLLOWERS. HE EXPLAINED MANY THINGS TO THEM ABOUT THE SCRIPTURES, BUT ONLY WHEN HE BROKE BREAD WITH THEM BEFORE DISAPPEARING DID THEY REALIZE WHO THIS STRANGER REALLY WAS–JESUS HIMSELF!

THAT SAME EVENING, JESUS APPEARED TO THE DISCIPLES. AT FIRST, THEY COULDN'T BELIEVE HE WAS REAL. BUT HE REASSURED THEM AND SHOWED THEM HIS SCARS. "TOUCH ME AND SEE," HE SAID. "A GHOST DOESN'T HAVE FLESH AND BONES!"

THOMAS WAS NOT WITH THE OTHERS, AND HE WOULDN'T BELIEVE THEM. BUT A WEEK LATER, JESUS WAS AMONG THEM AGAIN. TURNING TO THOMAS HE SAID, "PUT YOUR FINGER IN THE WOUNDS IN MY HANDS. REACH OUT AND FEEL MY SIDE. STOP DOUBTING AND BELIEVE!" AND THOMAS FELL TO HIS KNEES, OVERCOME WITH JOY.

JESUS SAID, "YOU ONLY BELIEVED BECAUSE YOU SAW ME YOURSELF. HOW BLESSED WILL PEOPLE BE WHO BELIEVE WITHOUT EVEN SEEING!"

ON THAT DARK FRIDAY JESUS DIED, AND HIS BODY WAS PLACED IN A TOMB. SATURDAY WAS SAD AND TERRIBLE AS THOSE WHO LOVED HIM TRIED TO UNDERSTAND HOW HIS DEATH COULD POSSIBLY BE GOD'S PLAN. THEN SUNDAY CAME–THAT THIRD DAY–AND THE TOMB WAS FOUND EMPTY. JESUS HAD RISEN TO LIFE AGAIN! JUST AS HE HAD SAID HE WOULD. NOT EVEN DEATH WAS STRONGER THAN HIM!

AND BECAUSE JESUS ROSE, SO CAN THOSE WHO LOVE AND FOLLOW HIM (JOHN 11:25–26). DEATH ISN'T THE END. IT'S A WONDERFUL NEW BEGINNING . . . IN FOREVER WITH HIM!

The Ascension

JESUS AND HIS FRIENDS WERE ON A HILLSIDE OUTSIDE JERUSALEM. THE TIME HAD COME FOR JESUS TO LEAVE THE WORLD. IN THE TIME SINCE HIS RESURRECTION, HE HAD MADE MANY THINGS CLEARER TO THEM. NOW HE TOLD THEM TO WAIT FOR THE GIFT THAT HIS FATHER WOULD SEND THEM: "FOR SOON YOU WILL BE BAPTIZED WITH THE HOLY SPIRIT. THEN YOU MUST SPREAD MY MESSAGE NOT ONLY IN JERUSALEM AND JUDAH AND SAMARIA, BUT IN EVERY COUNTRY."

HE HELD UP HIS HANDS TO BLESS THEM AND THEN, BEFORE THEIR EYES, HE WAS TAKEN UP TO HEAVEN, AND A CLOUD HID HIM FROM SIGHT.

AS THEY LOOKED UPWARDS IN WONDER, SUDDENLY TWO MEN IN WHITE STOOD BESIDE THEM. "WHY ARE YOU LOOKING AT THE SKY? JESUS HAS BEEN TAKEN FROM YOU INTO HEAVEN, BUT HE WILL COME BACK AGAIN IN THE SAME WAY THAT HE LEFT!"

JESUS HAD LEFT THE EARTHLY WORLD, BUT HE HAD PROMISED THAT HIS FATHER WOULD SEND A GIFT. TEN DAYS LATER, THE DISCIPLES WERE TOGETHER WHEN SUDDENLY THE HOUSE WAS FILLED WITH THE SOUND OF A MIGHTY WIND COMING FROM HEAVEN. AS THEY WATCHED, TONGUES OF FIRE SEEMED TO REST ON EACH PERSON THERE. THEY WERE ALL FILLED WITH THE HOLY SPIRIT, AND BEGAN TO SPEAK IN DIFFERENT LANGUAGES—ONES THEY HAD NEVER SPOKEN BEFORE OR STUDIED!

HEARING THE COMMOTION, A CROWD GATHERED OUTSIDE. PEOPLE WERE AMAZED WHEN THE DISCIPLES CAME OUT AND BEGAN TALKING IN DIFFERENT LANGUAGES, TELLING PEOPLE OF ALL NATIONALITIES ABOUT GOD'S PLAN FOR JESUS, AND ABOUT HOW GOD HAD RAISED JESUS TO LIFE. MANY FELT DREADFUL ABOUT WHAT HAD HAPPENED, BUT PETER KNEW THERE WAS SOMETHING THEY COULD DO ABOUT IT.

"IF YOU'RE REALLY SORRY," HE TOLD THEM, "THEN REPENT. BE BAPTIZED IN THE NAME OF JESUS CHRIST, AND YOUR SINS WILL BE FORGIVEN. AND YOU WILL RECEIVE THE GIFT OF THE HOLY SPIRIT. THIS PROMISE ISN'T JUST FOR YOU, BUT FOR YOUR CHILDREN, AND FOR PEOPLE WHO ARE FAR AWAY—GOD'S GIFT IS FOR EVERYONE!"

THIS WAS THE BEGINNING OF THE SPREAD OF CHRISTIANITY AND THE BIRTH OF THE CHURCH. THE STORY OF JESUS IS THE STORY OF SALVATION. THE PATH TO GOD IS THROUGH CHRIST. GOD'S GIFT IS THERE FOR EVERYONE WHO BELIEVES!

JESUS RETURNED TO HEAVEN, BUT HE DIDN'T LEAVE HIS FOLLOWERS ALONE. GOD SENT THEM A GIFT—AND IT'S A GIFT HE STILL GIVES TO THOSE WHO TRUST THEIR HEARTS AND LIVES TO HIM.

WHEN YOU CHOOSE TO LOVE, OBEY, AND FOLLOW HIM, GOD SENDS HIS HOLY SPIRIT TO LIVE INSIDE YOU. NOT JUST WITH YOU OR NEAR YOU, BUT ACTUALLY INSIDE YOU, SO THAT YOU ARE NEVER WITHOUT HIM. THE SPIRIT WORKS THROUGH GOD'S WORD AND HIS PEOPLE TO TEACH AND COMFORT AND STRENGTHEN YOU (JOHN 14:26). SO THAT YOU NEVER HAVE TO FACE THIS LIFE OR ITS STRUGGLES ALONE.

THIS IS HOW YOU SHOULD PRAY...

Love.
It's the reason God sent His Son to this earth. It's the reason Jesus died on the cross for your sins. And it's the reason He rose up from the grave, overcoming death and opening up the gates of heaven to you. Because God loves you that much (John 3:16).
Are you ready to love Him too? Talk to Him. Read His Word. Let Him show you the way.

Father,
I believe you sent Your Son, Jesus, to save me, and I want You to be the Lord of my life. Teach me to follow You—to love and obey and worship You in everything I do and say. I give my heart and my life to You.
It's in the holy name of Jesus that I pray.
Amen.